Linda Ronstadt

with Nelson Riddle  and his Orchestra

Photography:
Front Cover: Mark Hanauer
Page 2: Brian Aris
Pages 3, 4: Bob Blakeman
Cover Art Direction/Design: Kosh

CONTENTS

Due to copyright restrictions, "What'll I Do" is not included in this folio.

GUESS I'LL HANG MY TEARS OUT TO DRY

Words by
SAMMY CAHN

Music by
JULE STYNE

Slowly, with expression

har - bor feels. When I want rain,

I get sun-ny weath-er; I'm just as blue as the sky. Since love is gone, can't

pull my-self to-geth-er. Guess I'll hang my tears out to dry. Friends ask me out,

I tell them I'm bus-y, so I must get a new al-i-bi. I stay at home, and

I DON'T STAND A GHOST OF A CHANCE

Words by
BING CROSBY and NED WASHINGTON

Music by
VICTOR YOUNG

12

Slow four

If you'd sur-ren-der for a ten-der___ kiss or two,

(Inst.) _____

you might dis-cov-er that I'm the lov-er

meant for you, and I'll be true.

But what's the good of

schem-ing?___ I know I must be dream-ing,___

I'VE GOT A CRUSH ON YOU

Music and Lyrics by
GEORGE GERSHWIN and IRA GERSHWIN

WHAT'S NEW?

Words by
JOHNNY BURKE

Music by
BOB HAGGART

LOVER MAN
(OH, WHERE CAN YOU BE?)

Words and Music by
JIMMY DAVIS, ROGER "RAM" RAMIREZ
and JIMMY SHERMAN

CRAZY HE CALLS ME

Words by
BOB RUSSELL

Music by
CARL SIGMAN

GOODBYE

Words and Music by
GORDON JENKINS

SOMEONE TO WATCH OVER ME

Music and Lyrics by
GEORGE GERSHWIN and IRA GERSHWIN

WHEN I FALL IN LOVE

Words by
EDWARD HEYMAN

Music by
VICTOR YOUNG

SKYLARK

Words by
JOHNNY MERCER

Music by
HOAGY CARMICHAEL

Moderately slow

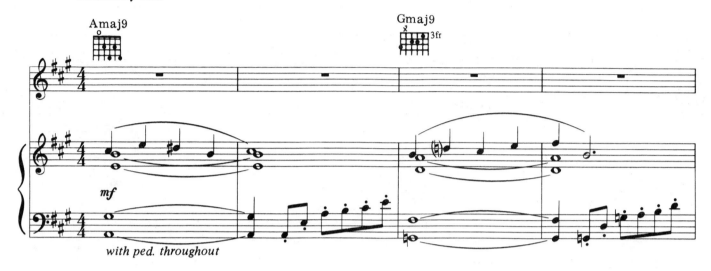

with ped. throughout

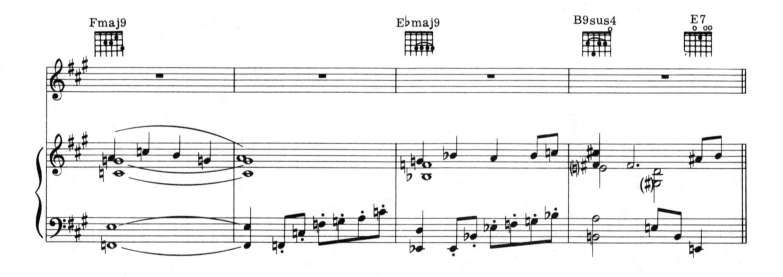

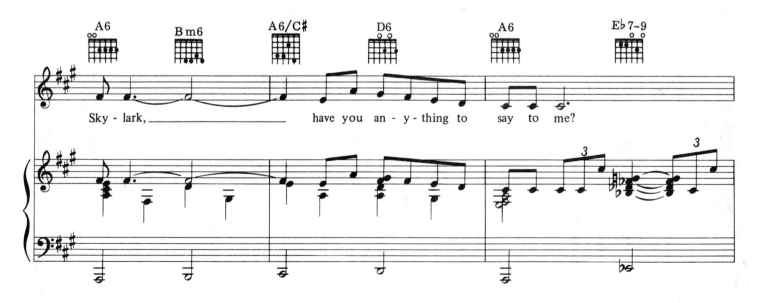

Sky - lark, _____ have you an - y - thing to say to me?

MEAN TO ME

Words and Music by
FRED E. AHLERT and ROY TURK

47

WHEN YOUR LOVER HAS GONE

Words and Music by
E.A. SWAN

oft-en may per-ish and leave you with cas-tles in air.

Very free

Slowly in tour

When you're a-lone who cares for moon-lit skies?_

When you're a-lone the mag-ic moon-light dies.

IT NEVER ENTERED MY MIND

Words by
LORENZ HART

Music by
RICHARD RODGERS

I'M A FOOL TO WANT YOU

**Words and Music by
JACK WOLF, JOEL HERRON
and FRANK SINATRA**

YOU TOOK ADVANTAGE OF ME

Words by
LORENZ HART

Music by
RICHARD RODGERS

to fall? — I have — no will, — you've made your kill — 'cause you
some - how. — So what's — the use, — you've cooked my goose — 'cause you

took ad - van - tage of me.
took ad - van - tage of me.

I'm so hot and both - ered that I don't know my el - bow — from my ear. —

CAN'T WE BE FRIENDS?

Words by
PAUL JAMES

Music by
KAY SWIFT

I thought I'd found the man of my dreams,___ now it seems
I thought for once it could-n't go wrong,___ not for long!

SOPHISTICATED LADY

Words and Music by
DUKE ELLINGTON, IRVING MILLS
and MITCHELL PARISH

MY OLD FLAME

Words and Music by
ARTHUR JOHNSTON and
SAM COSLOW

LUSH LIFE

Words and Music by
BILLY STRAYHORN

FALLING IN LOVE AGAIN
(CAN'T HELP IT)

Words and Music by
FREDERICK HOLLANDER

Revised Lyric by
SAMMY LERNER

Medium Jazz Beat

No Chord

What am I to do? Can't help it.

Fall-ing in love a-gain,___ nev-er want-ed to.

(Instrumental) _____

What am I ___ to do? Can't help it.

Love's al-ways been my game,___ play it how___ I

WHEN YOU WISH UPON A STAR

Words and Music by
NED WASHINGTON and LEIGH HARLINE

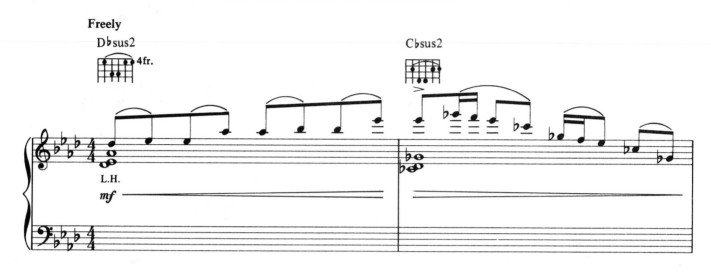

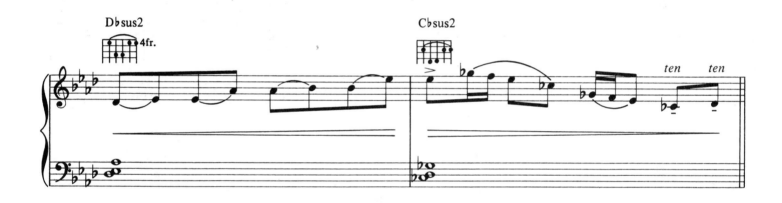

When you wish up-on a star, makes no dif-f'rence

BEWITCHED, BOTHERED & BEWILDERED

Words by
LORENZ HART

Music by
RICHARD RODGERS

YOU GO TO MY HEAD

Words by
HAVEN GILLESPIE

Music by
J. FRED COOTS

BUT NOT FOR ME

Music and Lyrics by
GEORGE GERSHWIN and IRA GERSHWIN

MY FUNNY VALENTINE

Words by
LORENZ HART

Music by
RICHARD RODGERS

dim - wit - ted friends the pic - ture_____ thou hast made; thy

va - cant brow and thy tou - sled hair con - ceal thy good in - tent. Thou

no - ble, up - right, truth - ful, sin - cere and slight - ly_____ dop - ey gent, you're

Slowly, with a lot of feeling

my fun - ny val - en - tine, sweet com - ic

111

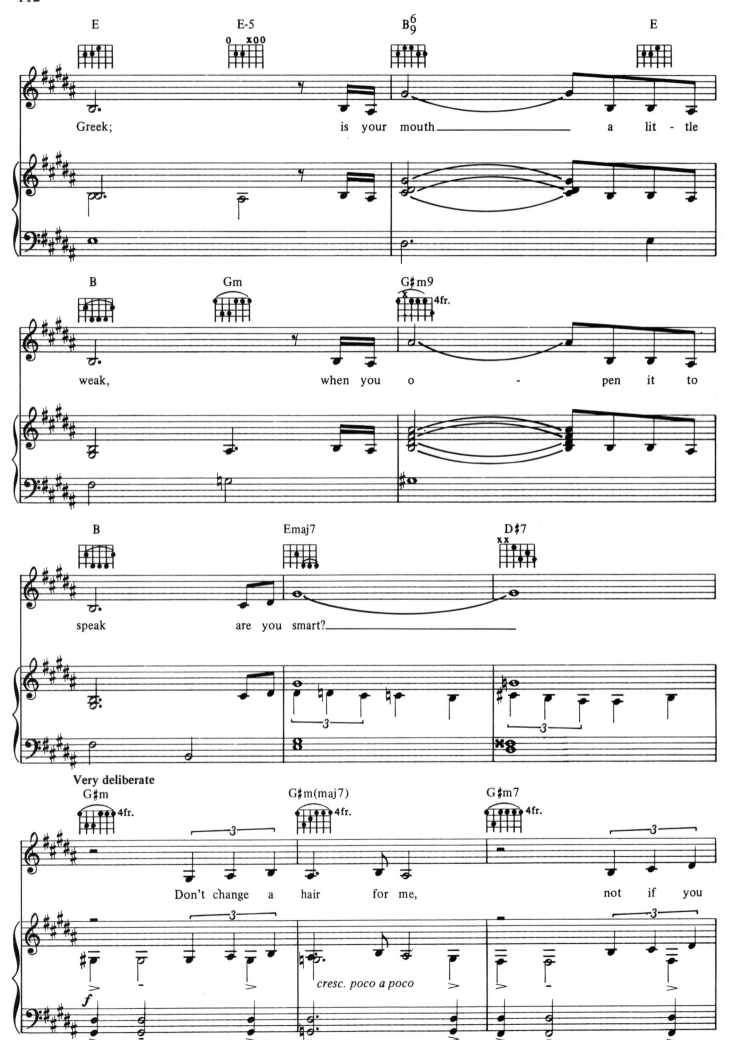

AM I BLUE?

Words by
GRANT CLARKE

Music by
HARRY AKST

115

I LOVE YOU FOR SENTIMENTAL REASONS

Words by
DEEK WATSON

Music by
WILLIAM BEST

STRAIGHTEN UP AND FLY RIGHT

Words and Music by
NAT KING COLE and IRVING MILLS

LITTLE GIRL BLUE

Words by
LORENZ HART

Music by
RICHARD RODGERS

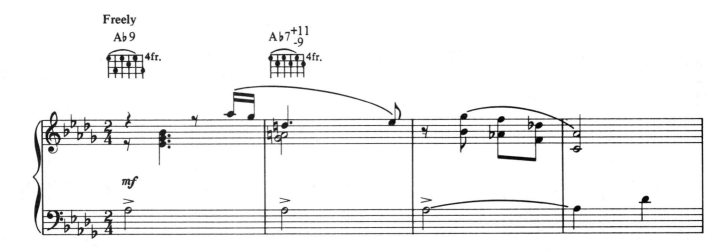

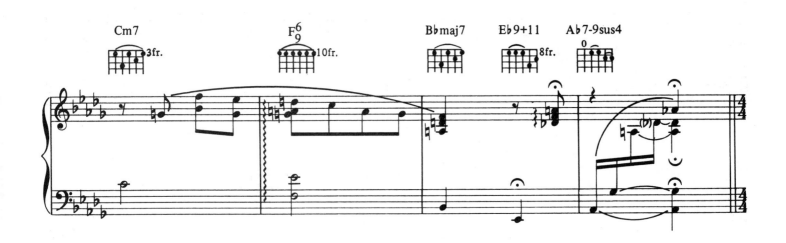

Sit there___ and count your fin - gers, what can you do?

Tempo I

D.S. ℅ al Coda ⊕

Eb9   A9   Db/Ab   Ebm/Ab   Fm/Ab   Ab7-9-5

gone are the tin - sel and gold.____

Coda

Db6   Db7-9   B9(addG♯)   A9(addF♯)   Db6   Bbm7

(Instr.)____ All you____ can

Ebm7   Db   Ebm   Gm7-5   Ab7sus4   Ab7   Ebm7   Ab9   Ab7-9

count on is the rain - drops that fall on lit - tle girl

rit.

a tempo
Db6   E+5   F♯/E   Db6

blue.____

'ROUND MIDNIGHT

Words by
BERNIE HANIGHEN

Music by
COOTIE WILLIAMS and **THELONIOUS MONK**

135

I GET ALONG WITHOUT YOU VERY WELL

(Except Sometimes)

Words and Music by
HOAGY CARMICHAEL

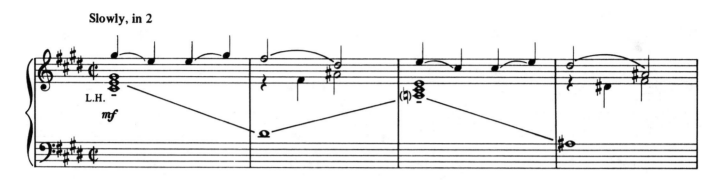

I get a-long with-out you—— ver-y well, of course I
I've for-got-ten you, just—— like I should, of course I